# DEOWULF

*Illustrated by*

Li Sidong

*Retold by*

Jacqueline Morley

*Series created and designed by*

David Salariya

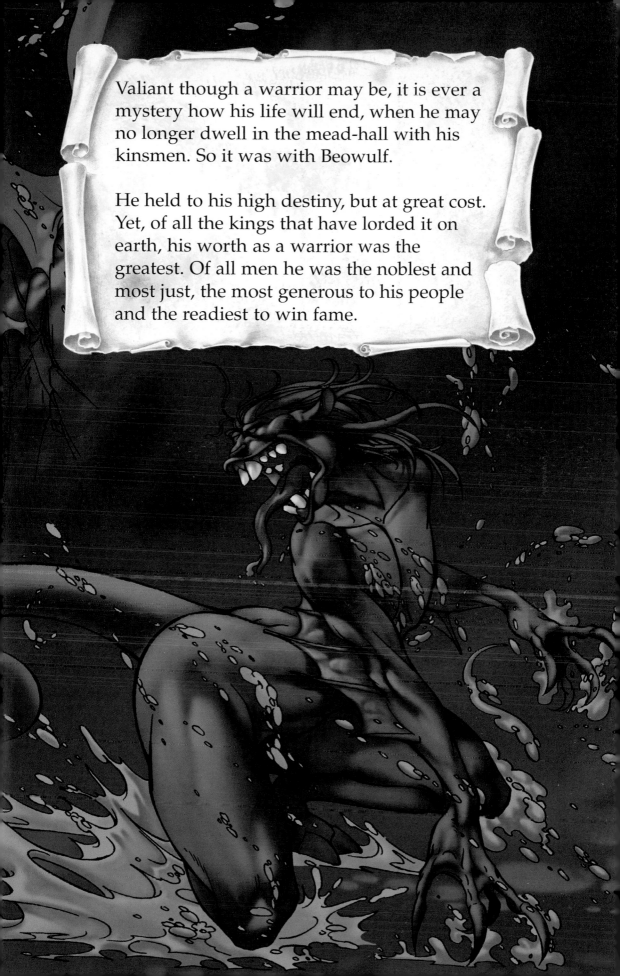

Valiant though a warrior may be, it is ever a mystery how his life will end, when he may no longer dwell in the mead-hall with his kinsmen. So it was with Beowulf.

He held to his high destiny, but at great cost. Yet, of all the kings that have lorded it on earth, his worth as a warrior was the greatest. Of all men he was the noblest and most just, the most generous to his people and the readiest to win fame.

# CHARACTERS

## THE GEATS

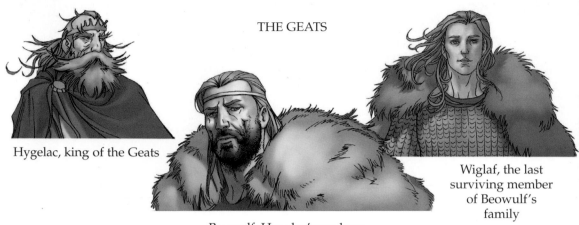

Hygelac, king of the Geats

Beowulf, Hygelac's nephew

Wiglaf, the last surviving member of Beowulf's family

## THE DANES

Hrothgar, king of the Danes

Wealhtheow, his young queen

Unferth, a jealous, boastful warrior

## THE MONSTERS

Grendel

Grendel's mother

The dragon

# FEASTING AND SONG

In England long ago, in the days when the Angles and the Saxons[1] were free people (before the Normans[2] took their land), a lord was holding a feast in his great hall. Like all wealthy nobles he kept in his household a bard – a skilled musician and teller of tales – to entertain his guests. The bard would sing in verse to the sound of his lyre,[3] telling well-loved stories of the old gods and heroes of the past. These tales were ancient even in Anglo-Saxon times.

> A song! A song of the days when men were truly great. Give us a tale of heroes, of battles and of monsters!

When the meal was over the guests called for the bard to begin.

> I will tell you a tale of long ago, when demons prowled the earth.

> Now listen – listen all!

There was silence in the hall.

> Hear how the Danes of the north – a great warrior nation – were beset by a fiend the bravest of them dared not face. Then a hero crossed the sea to save them. His name was BEOWULF. Hear his deeds!

1. the Angles and the Saxons: peoples from northern Germany who invaded England in the 5th century AD. Their language, Anglo-Saxon, was the ancestor of modern English.
2. the Normans: a people of Scandinavian descent who had settled in northern France and spoke a dialect of French. They invaded England in 1066.
3. lyre: a stringed instrument, played rather like a harp, with strings supported by two arms and a crossbar.

# THE GOLDEN HALL

But first I must tell you of the golden hall called Heorot, and how it came to be built.

It happened that in far-off times the Danes were kingless, having driven their unworthy ruler into exile. After this they suffered many hardships. Again and again their neighbours attacked them, for enemies do not fear a people without a leader.

Then one day a small boat was washed up on their shore. It had neither steersman nor crew.

Inside the boat a boy-child lay asleep upon a sheaf of wheat. The Danes took him in and cared for him.

They named the boy Scyld Scefing.[1] He grew to be a fearless warrior, a leader who made the Danes' enemies tremble. Clans[2] far and wide paid him tribute.[3] He was a great king.

1. Scyld Scefing: Shield, son of the sheaf.
2. clans: groups of related families.
3. tribute: gifts given by subjects to their lord or ruler.

When Scyld died, his followers laid him in a ship, as he had wished, and let the waves carry him away as they had brought him. No-one can say where that voyage ended.

Of the great Danish kings descended from Scyld, the noblest was Hrothgar, son of Halfdane.

So many men flocked to serve him that no building could house them. So Hrothgar ordered a great hall to be built.

Soon a glorious new mead-hall[1] shone in the sunlight. Hrothgar named it Heorot.[2] It was both throne-room and feasting hall, a fit place for a lord to entertain his followers in.

Laughter and song rang out daily from Heorot and the good king was glad.

But there was a listener lurking in the dark beyond its doors – one who hated happiness and waited to destroy it...

1. mead-hall: a hall where warriors drink mead, an alcoholic drink made from honey.
2. Heorot: The name means 'hart' or 'deer' – a royal beast.

# THE MONSTER IN THE NIGHT

This demon was called Grendel – a flesh-eating ogre that rose from the marshes. He sprang from the race of fiends that served Cain,[1] the first of all murderers, who was cursed by God.

He came in the night, while Hrothgar's warriors lay asleep in the great hall.

He seized sleepers by the hair, tore them to pieces and thrust thirty mangled bodies in his pouch.

Back in his lair he feasted on the gobbets.[2]

God save us! What sort of enemy was this?

Daylight showed Hrothgar the night's horrors: blood-splattered walls and footprints oozing red.

---

1. Cain: According to the Bible, Cain was the first son of Adam and Eve. He murdered his brother Abel out of jealousy. In Christian tradition he is sometimes seen as the father of all evil.
2. gobbets: lumps of flesh.

Night after night the demon came, till no-one dared sleep in the hall. The ageing king and his men were no match for this evil.

For twelve years the Danes lived in terror of Grendel. The greatest hall in the world stood empty. Yet, though Grendel ruled it, he could not touch the throne of the good king. Some power held him off.

Hygelac's young kinsman[2] Beowulf listened closely.

The story of the Danes' sufferings was told in every land. Across the sea in the realm of the Geats[1] a bard sang the tale at the court of king Hygelac.

Fiends[3] did not frighten him!

My lord, grant me leave to sail to Denmark and offer the strength of my arm to King Hrothgar.

Go and gain glory. But better still, return safely.

To Denmark!

Beowulf hand-picked fourteen of his bravest comrades to sail with him.

1. Geats: a people who lived in what is now southern Sweden.
2. kinsman: relative.
3. fiends: demons.

# A Hero's Pledge

As they beached their boat upon the Danish shore, Beowulf and his men were fiercely challenged.

Satisfied they meant no harm, the watchman directed them to Heorot.

Among the Danes at table sat Unferth, a jealous man who did not like the favour shown by Hrothgar to a stranger.

If you can do better, Unferth, why haven't you killed Grendel yourself?

Then everyone jeered at Unferth.

Boaster!

Coward!

Good humour was restored as Hrothgar's young queen Wealhtheow entered, bearing the ceremonial mead-cup to honour the guests.

Drink, my lord, and may your heart be lightened.

Next she offered the brimming cup to Beowulf. After he had drunk, he made a solemn vow, aloud, before everyone in the hall.

Guard Heorot well, for it is the greatest of houses. Whatever you wish is yours if you win through.

I have come here for one thing only: to kill Grendel — or to die here, in this hall.

When night came, the Danes went to rest elsewhere, in safety. Hrothgar left Beowulf in charge of Heorot. He had never entrusted his hall to another man before.

# THE SCREAM

Beowulf ordered his men to rest while he kept watch. He handed them his sword and armour.

This brute is ignorant of weapons, so I shall fight him without them.

The Geats lay down to sleep uneasily with their swords ready to hand.

Then from the moors, through the mist, Grendel came loping.

Raging for blood, he ripped open the door...

...and in an instant tore a sleeping Geat to shreds.

Beowulf lunged and seized him in an armlock.

Every timber of Heorot shook as if about to split apart, as man and monster crashed about the hall.

How can we help?

No earthly weapon has power to harm Grendel.

AÏEEEEE!

Then came a scream so hellish that the Danes, asleep far off, sat up in terror in their beds.

Beowulf had wrenched away the monster's arm!

Grendel knew he had a death wound as he slunk away to his lair in a trail of blood.

This shows how Beowulf keeps his promises.

Beowulf ordered the arm to be nailed above the entrance to Heorot.

# REJOICING IN HEOROT

When morning came, the Danes saw the arm and knew who had won the fight.

Beowulf has cleansed Heorot!

A party of warriors followed Grendel's trail to a dark mere[1] in the forest.

The water's thick with blood. He's dead.

In high spirits, they raced each other back to tell the king.

Let's get the news to every village!

On hearing of the night's happenings, Hrothgar was deeply moved.

Noblest of men, God sent you to me. I adopt you in my heart as a dear son.

I have one big regret: I cannot lay the body before you. But Grendel is dead for sure.

1: mere: a marshy lake.

All day long crowds thronged to see the dreadful arm. Every spike upon it was like barbed steel. Unferth looked and turned away without a word.

No weapon could touch it.

When the hall had been set straight, the king ordered a great victory feast.

A small reward for your great service to us all.

He presented Beowulf with a golden battle-standard and rich armour, together with eight proud horses and a costly saddle on which the king himself had ridden to battle.

The queen gave Beowulf a magnificent gold neck-ring, fit for a god. It had no equal on earth.

That was a happy feast — for men do not see into the future.

Wear it for luck and for a lifetime's blessing.

That ring was to pass to Hygelac the Geat, and brought him no joy. It was torn from his neck as he lay dying in Frisia,[1] on the fatal raid that brought his people so much harm, as I will tell.[2]

1. Frisia: a land which stretched from present-day Denmark to the Netherlands.
2. as I will tell: See page 30. The *Beowulf* story has many digressions in which the narrator tells, or refers to, various adventures of the Geats and the Danes.

# The Avenger

Grendel was indeed dead, but not forgotten. He had a mother. In the depth of the mere she brooded on her son's slaughter and swore revenge.

Racked with grief, and ravenous,[1] she came to Heorot next night.

Hrothgar's warriors, happily returned to their hall, were sleeping when she struck.

As swiftly as she had come, she vanished onto the moors…

She snatched a victim and tore her son's arm from the door

…and sank into the black water of the mere.

1. ravenous: extremely hungry.

The king was brought the news at dawn. The victim was his closest friend.

Beowulf was summoned from his sleep by the desperate king.

Aeschere, my lord — snatched in the night!

Alas for the Danes! Sorrow has returned. Aeschere, my wisest counsellor and friend, is dead.

Too late, the old king now remembered the country people's tales of two dread prowlers , male and female, seen in the wilds.

They dwell apart among the wolves...

...deep in a mere so grim, a stag would sooner face a pack of hounds than flee into its waters.

Seek it for me if you dare.

At night the water burns uncannily.[1] It is an evil place.

I will reward you with coffers of gold if you come back.

1. uncannily: in a mysterious, supernatural way.

# THE MERE

Beowulf was ready to face any terror.

Death waits for us all, so let him who can win glory.

He set off for the mere with his loyal Geats. Hrothgar and a party of Danes acted as their guides.

They entered a dismal wood whose frost-stiffened branches met over their heads. Knotted tree roots groped in the depths below.

At the mere's edge they stopped in horror.

Aeschere's head!

The sight filled every heart with rage. The Geats sounded their battle horns to challenge the monster that did such savagery.

The horn notes roused a host of hideous reptiles that lived in the waters. Beowulf slew one.

His men hauled it ashore and shuddered at the monstrous form.

Unferth the braggart now wanted to be generous. He lent Beowulf his sword – a famous one.

Without more words or hesitation, Beowulf plunged into the water.

Its name is Hrunting. It has never failed in battle.

Unferth was not man enough himself to use it in this task.

Protect my men if I do not return, and let my lord Hygelac have my treasure.

# THE WATER HAG

It was almost a day before he reached the bottom. Grendel's mother sensed his coming.

She was waiting to grab him.

The creatures of the depths attacked him as he struggled.

In the hag's lair he tore himself from her grasp.

CLANGG!

He swung Hrunting and brought the blade down on her head.

The blow had no effect. Hrunting could not bite her!

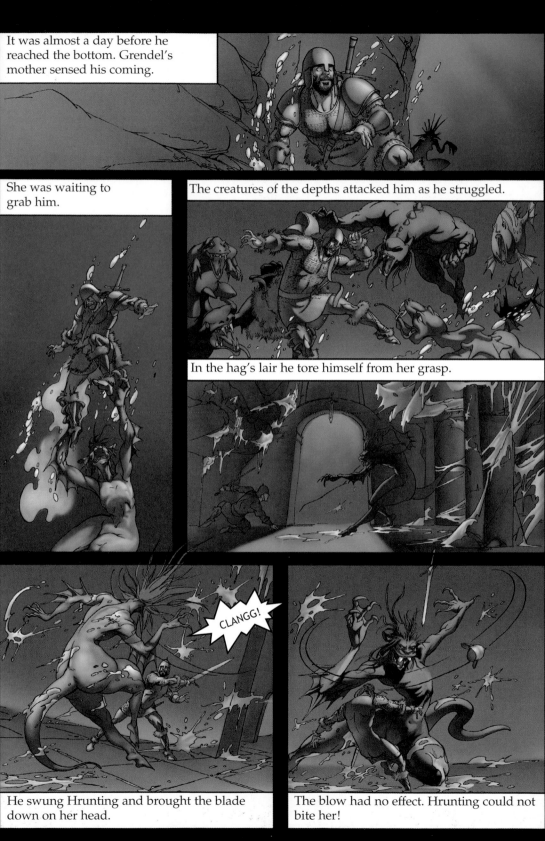

Now there was nothing he could do but wrestle with the fiend.

She locked her arms around him.

He stumbled backwards. She stabbed repeatedly.

His chain mail saved him.

He snatched down the giant weapon...

...and severed the monster's neck.

On the wall of the cave hung an ancient sword. It was the work of giants.

# BLOOD IN THE WATER

With the death of the monster, everything brightened, as if the sun had come out.

With sword still drawn, Beowulf explored the underwater hall.

**Their victims! What a hideous sight.**

Brave man that he was, he shuddered at what he saw.

He saw vaults[1] full of treasure but touched none of it.

Then he came upon the thing he sought.

He struck in a fury.

**Grendel dead!**

**This is for Hrothgar's sake!**

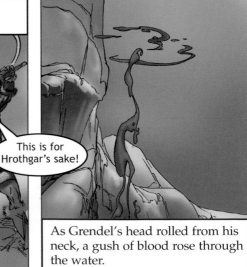

As Grendel's head rolled from his neck, a gush of blood rose through the water.

1. vaults: storerooms for valuables.

Beowulf stared at the blade that had made the stroke. It was melting away like gory[1] icicles.

The men keeping watch above saw the waters reddening.

An evil sign! Blood welling up!

Hrothgar bowed his head. He had feared the worst and it had come about: Beowulf was dead.

Let us return. We can do nothing more. Nothing but go to Heorot and mourn.

As dusk fell, Hrothgar and his Danes went home with heavy hearts.

The Geats remained. They would not give up hope, and watched the waters for some sign.

1. gory: bloody.

# BEOWULF'S TROPHY

Beowulf swam upwards through untroubled water. Every evil creature was gone.

There's something moving through the water.

It's him!

See here! A face to make the king smile!

His men ran with shouts of joy to pull him from the water.

Good men! You waited for me. You knew I would return.

Never doubted it. We Geats can show those Danes a thing or two.

As they left the mere it no longer seemed threatening. The woods were smiling and the waters calm.

It took four strong men to carry Grendel's head to Heorot on their spears.

The sound of triumphant shouting in the darkness brought watchmen running from the gate.

They stared in disbelief.

A monster coming on stilts!

And that's Beowulf leading it!

A guard raced to tell the king.

Beowulf returned! May all the gods be thanked!

Danes, look on your enemy and fear him no more.

Women screamed and warriors drew back.

The shouts that greeted Beowulf turned to silence as he dragged the horrendous head across the hall.

# HROTHGAR'S WARNING

Horror in the hall was followed by rejoicing as Beowulf described his battle with the mother-monster.

*My friend and best of men, never will the Danes forget the debt they owe you.*

*It is a rare weapon made for giants. I thank you.*

*It was a hard-fought, desperate affair that might have gone badly.*

Beowulf presented the king with the hilt of the ancient sword that had saved his life.

Hrothgar then rose to speak. He foretold that Beowulf would make a great ruler.

Every voice in the hall was hushed to listen to the king, who spoke with the voice of wisdom and experience. He followed his praise with a warning to Beowulf.

*He is a man born to distinction, courageous and resolute.*[1]

*Good and brave though you be, Beowulf, remember courage alone does not make a good ruler.*

*Remember your strength is only lent to you. It is worth nothing if not used wisely. Life is short; soon illness or the sword will lay you low.*

*Too many fine men have been ruined by ambition. Do not let greed and battle-lust into your heart.*

*Use your time well, for death will arise, dear warrior, to sweep you away.*

---

1. resolute: determined.

28

Beowulf listened closely to the wise old king, who led him to a seat of honour in the hall. Every warrior praised him.

Now join us in our victory feast.

Now Beowulf's men were eager to be home. Their ship was loaded with Hrothgar's gifts: treasure, horses and war gear.

The old king embraced Beowulf and wept, knowing in his heart that he would not live to see him again.

If anything should happen to King Hygelac, the Geats won't find a better man to lead them than you.

The sail-ropes tightened and the curved prow broke the waves. Beowulf gazed seaward, thinking of the old king's words.

Stiff winds drove the sea-skimmer[1] northwards until the Geats sighted the familiar cliffs of home.

I am happy to present my lord with tokens of King Hrothgar's gratitude.

Beowulf loyally gave Hrothgar's gifts to his overlord,[2] King Hygelac. Hygelac returned many of them to Beowulf, but he kept the splendid neck-ring for himself.[3]

1. sea-skimmer: ship. Phrases of this kind, known as *kennings*, are typical of Anglo-Saxon poetry.
2. overlord: the person to whom he owes loyalty.
3. kept . . . for himself: see page 17.

# BEOWULF THE KING

In the years that followed, Beowulf had good reason to remember the wise words of Hrothgar. King Hygelac was greedy for gold and heedless of his people's wellbeing.

He boasted of the booty he took in foreign lands, but he made the Geats' name hated there.

Hygelac was killed raiding in Frisia and the golden neck-ring, pledge of friendship, became enemy plunder.

This is a bad day's work. The Frisians will not forgive us. Unless we make them fear us, they will take a terrible revenge.

Hygelac's young son Headred was a weakling. Even his mother thought him unfit to rule. Before long, he was killed fighting the Swedes. Now Hrothgar's prophecy was fulfilled: Beowulf was king, and showed how a true protector of his people should govern.

Beowulf ruled the Geats wisely for fifty years. But his doom[1] awaited him, as it does for all of us.

The fate of this great king lay in the hands of a pitiful wretch — a slave on the run from his master.

He was clambering up a cliffside, seeking a place to hide, when he found a hidden opening in the rocks.

1. doom: fate.

He found himself in a cavern filled with gold.

I'm a rich man! I can buy my freedom.

Then he saw a sleeping dragon coiled round the heap of gold!

He took the goblet and ran.

When the dragon awoke, it knew it had been robbed. A terrible rage possessed it.

Unable to find the thief, it torched everything in sight: homes, people, cattle, trees. The dragon became a nightly terror.

The entire land was swathed in flame. Beowulf's royal hall was burned.

# THE LAST CHALLENGE

King Beowulf, now an old man, was plunged into deep gloom by the night raider. It was not the dragon itself that troubled him – he had no fear of it. His dread was that in some way he was to blame for its coming.

Have I done wrong in God's sight? Is this the punishment?

Finally he put such broodings from his mind. He made a solemn vow before his men.

I am the guardian of my people. It is for me to face this enemy — alone.

The boldest of his warriors would not have dared so much. His counsellors feared to lose so good a king.

Instead of the usual wooden shield, the king ordered one of iron to be made.

Molten venom[1] will not harm it — if any man can lift it!

Never fear that.

Beowulf set off, with a force of eleven men, to find the dragon.

The slave led them to a clifftop and pointed to the dragon's lair below.

Till now my strength has never failed me. Is this the moment which King Hrothgar taught me to expect?

Beowulf stood for a moment, gazing out to sea, as if lost in thought.

1. molten venom: the dragon's fiery, poisonous breath.

The old king sat for some time on the clifftop, weighing up his life, past and present. He knew he had come to a place where a hard bargain must be made.

He was heavy-hearted, troubled yet ready.

It shall be as the overseer of all men[1] decides.

He sprang to his feet suddenly, kingly and resolute.

His kinsman Wiglaf, the youngest of his followers, handed him his great shield and helmet.

Let me go with you.

Beowulf would not allow it. He set off alone.

Wait where you are and do not fear for me. I shall bring my people freedom and much gold too — if fate allows.

Then he strode down the cliff face – no path for a coward.

He turned at the cliff brow to bid his dear companions farewell.

1. the overseer of all men: God.

# FLAME AND FURY

He saw flames issuing from the rocks and roared out a battle-challenge that echoed down the cave.

I shall fight the destroyer if it dares to face me!

Beowulf flung up his iron shield to guard his face.

The dragon writhed in fiendish contortions as it felt the strokes of Beowulf's sword. It torched him with a jet of fire.

Beowulf staggered back engulfed in flame, his shield and mail-shirt glowing red-hot.

His men saw their leader trapped within walls of fire. They turned and fled...

...all except one: Wiglaf, the youngest, who had never yet been tested in battle.

He saw the dragon rearing for a final strike, and, drawing his sword, he ran into the flames.

Cowards! Would you leave him?

# A Fight to the Death

Wiglaf's wooden shield was burnt to ashes in an instant.

But that instant was enough for Beowulf to recover.

Wiglaf! Get behind me!

My shield shall do for both of us.

Wiglaf was helpless, his hands too blistered to hold a weapon.

Together they went forward, keeping the shield raised against an avalanche of flame.

His blade snapped in two upon its skull.

Beowulf struck the dragon's head a whistling blow.

His hand went to his dagger…

…but before he could use it the dragon clamped its fangs into his neck.

Wiglaf saw the hero's life-blood gushing out.

With his last strength Beowulf drove his dagger deep into the monster's soft underbelly.

It was a death-blow.

# A Hero Departs

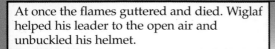

At once the flames guttered and died. Wiglaf helped his leader to the open air and unbuckled his helmet.

"Do this for me: let me look upon the treasure."

"I feel the dragon's venom working in me."

"Let me wash the wound."

In desperate haste, fearing to find his hero dead on his return, Wiglaf dragged chests of precious objects from the cave.

"I have ruled well and fought to save my people. That is my comfort."

The old lord gazed sadly at the gold. What use was it to him?

"I have given my last breath to win this fortune. Now I leave it to my people."

"You are the last of our line,[1] Wiglaf. Fate has sent all my other kinsmen to their doom and I must follow them."

"Miserable cowards!"

"Who's going to fear the Geats when this gets out?"

Now the cowards who had turned tail returned and saw that their leader had met a noble death. Wiglaf did not hide his contempt for them.

"I'd sooner die than live with shame like yours."

1. the last of our line: the last member of our family.

The Geats built a huge pyre,[1] hung with shields and shining armour, and laid their great leader upon it.

Smoke darkened the sky as the flames took hold.

The people stood in silence, feeling their great loss.

They knew that enemies are quick to attack a people without a leader.

The dragon's gold was buried with the king.

Beowulf's tomb was marked by a stone set on the headland, to guide his people safely home from sea.

For many days and nights his warriors kept vigil,[2] singing dirges[3] for their leader and praising his deeds.

He was of all kings the noblest and most just, the most generous to his people and the readiest to win fame.

1. pyre: a wooden platform used to cremate (burn) a dead body.
2. kept vigil: kept watch.
3. dirges: songs of mourning.

The End 39

The story of Beowulf the monster-slayer exists in only one copy, in an Anglo-Saxon manuscript (hand-written book) kept in the British Library in London. It is written in the form of a *lay* – a narrative poem sung by a bard. The poem opens with the traditional shout a bard gave to make sure he had everyone's attention: *Hwæt!*

## TELLING TALES

Storytelling was an important part of people's lives in the days when there were no ready-made forms of entertainment. A bard was a professional musician who chanted stories to the accompaniment of a lyre or harp – but storytelling of one kind or another went on whenever people were gathered together and had time to spare. The Norse (ancient Scandinavian) legends of gods and heroes had been handed down for generations in this way amongst the various Germanic peoples of northern Europe.

As the stories were told and retold, real characters and happenings – great kings and great victories – were woven into them, so that the legend of a dragon-slaying Scandinavian prince could become intertwined with real historical events. Beowulf, for example, fights in King Hygelac's raid on the Frisians. Hygelac was a real king who died in a raid in Frisia around AD 520.

## THE TELLER OF THE TALE

Who wrote *Beowulf*? We know nothing of the author of the poem except that he was English and – from comments

*The first page of the Beowulf manuscript. Compare the version in modern type on page 43.*

he makes in the poem – that he was Christian. The English, or Anglo-Saxons, were people from present-day Germany and Denmark who invaded southern Britain from the 5th century AD onwards, pushing the native Celtic peoples out into areas such as present-day Scotland, Wales and Cornwall.

The Anglo-Saxons gave up worshipping the Norse gods and converted to Christianity during the 7th century. Yet the *Beowulf* poet has chosen to tell a story from the pagan (non-Christian) past, about a Scandinavian hero. Perhaps he had heard a bard perform it, and been stirred by it. He certainly presents Beowulf's pagan world sympathetically, as a time when men were loyal and heroic in a very dangerous world. Sometimes he forgets himself and makes his characters speak as though they believed in a single God. At other times he expresses great pity for them and admiration for their bravery in facing death without hope, since they knew nothing of Christian salvation.

## THE WORLD OF *BEOWULF*

*Beowulf*, then, is an Anglo-Saxon poet's re-creation of life in Scandinavia several centuries before his own time – with monsters for good measure. Since the Anglo-Saxons were descendants of Scandinavian and Germanic tribes who had settled in Britain, they shared many of the same customs and beliefs. It would not be too hard for the poet to imagine the ancient Norse world.

It was a ruthless world of warring tribes, in which people survived by seeking the protection of a strong leader. Kings were no more than local warlords whose flair for leadership had enabled them to dominate a wider area than usual.

Warriors flocked to a successful leader because he could demand tributes (compulsory gifts) of gold from subject tribes – or seize it in raids on hostile ones. Gold, in the form of heavy rings or spirals, served as money, since there were no minted coins. Gold bound society together. Warriors won fame by gaining it for their lord; the lord won fame through his generosity in handing it out. A king's throne was known as his 'gift stool' from which the king, the 'ring-giver', rewarded his warriors.

The more fearless the fighter, the more treasure he deserved to get.

In this warrior world, the most joyful moments were those spent celebrating in the lord's great hall after some important event, such as a glorious raid or battle. All the warriors gathered together in fellowship around their leader. Deeds of outstanding bravery were honoured by the ring-giver who handed out rewards. There was light, warmth, feasting and song. The hall was the focus of a tribe's wellbeing. Heorot, the golden hall in *Beowulf*, is the symbol of King Hrothgar's greatness, which is why Grendel's occupation of it is so terrible.

But the brighter the hall, the greater the contrast with what lay outside. Tribes fought each other constantly, to get or keep the upper hand or to avenge an attack. The duty to seek vengeance led to constant blood feuds – long-running warfare between tribes or families that was difficult to stop. Every warrior knew that the bond between himself and his lord would almost certainly cost him his life.

The code of honour was strict. A warrior must fight to the death for his lord. It was a duty no-one questioned. The lord in his turn must never surrender. The most important thing in life was to be ready for death but not to fear it, and to perform such deeds that those who lived afterwards would remember you as a great warrior. This was Beowulf's creed.

# THE POEM OF *BEOWULF*

The only surviving copy of the poem is written in ink that has faded to brown, on vellum grey with age. (Vellum is good-quality parchment – a writing material made from animal skin which is stronger and longer-lasting than paper.)

And that manuscript has only survived by a whisker. It probably spent several centuries in some monastery library, and later passed through various hands into the famous collection of old books and documents known as the Cotton Library (brought together by the 17th-century collector Sir Robert Bruce Cotton and now in the British Library in London). In the 18th century the Cotton Library was rehoused in a building called Ashburnham House – not at all a lucky name, since a disastrous fire there in 1731 destroyed a quarter of the collection. The librarian was seen rushing out of the blaze in his nightgown and wig, hugging priceless manuscripts. *Beowulf* was among those saved, though badly scorched. As a result the edges of the pages have turned brittle and crumbled away over the years, and the ends of some of the lines have been lost. The damage has now been halted by modern conservation methods.

This manuscript has given Anglo-Saxon scholars a lot to puzzle over. From the style of the handwriting it seems to have been written in the late 10th or early 11th century. But when was the poem composed? Who was its author? Was it the man who wrote the manuscript we have, or was he just copying from an earlier version written by someone else who might or might not have been the poet himself? Most experts agree that the manuscript we have is a copy, written by two different scribes (professional copyists). As for the author, we can only say for certain that he was writing after the beginning of the 7th century – when the Anglo-Saxons began converting to Christianity – and before the date of the copy.

## THE LANGUAGE OF *BEOWULF*

The legends of the Norse gods and heroes survive today because at some stage they were written down. Here the poem *Beowulf* has a special claim to fame. Almost everything we know of Norse mythology comes from sources written in Iceland in the 13th and 14th centuries. *Beowulf* was written several centuries earlier, making it the earliest surviving record of Norse mythology. It is written in English and this wins it another first, as the earliest heroic poem in a modern European language.

Admittedly, few of today's English-speakers would recognise its language. Scholars term it Old English (or sometimes Anglo-Saxon), and it was the language spoken in most of England before the Norman Conquest of 1066. The Normans spoke a dialect of French, and brought so much French into the English language that it changed almost out of recognition, becoming medieval or Middle English. By Shakespeare's time this had developed into Modern English – and even his language can take some puzzling over today.

If you'd like a flavour of the poem as the author originally wrote it, here are its opening lines:

Hwæt! We Gardena  in geardagum,
þeodcyninga,  þrym gefrunon,
hu ða æþelingas  ellen fremedon.
Oft Scyld Scefing  sceaþena þreatum,
monegum mægþum,  meodosetla ofteah,
egsode eorlas.  Syððan ærest wearð
feasceaft funden,  he þæs frofre gebad,
weox under wolcnum,  weorðmyndum þah,
oðþæt him æghwylc  þara ymbsittendra
ofer hronrade  hyran scolde,
gomban gyldan.  þæt wæs god cyning!

You may have recognised the last four words: 'That was [a] good king!' But you can see that if you want to enjoy the poem you'll either have to become a serious student of Anglo-Saxon or use a translation.

But translators face problems too. It is difficult to create the poem's equivalent in modern verse because Anglo-Saxon poetry follows completely different rules. It doesn't rhyme and it doesn't have a regular beat. Instead, each line is formed of two phrases which are offset against each other according to strict rules which produce a different rhythm from line to line. Stressed syllables within a line *alliterate* (begin with the same letter), and this letter is always different from one line to the next. If you read the excerpt out loud with this in mind, you may be able to hear how the poetry works, even without understanding the words. The two strange letters þ and ð are both pronounced 'th', and æ is a sound midway between the vowels in 'bat' and 'bet'.

There have been more than a hundred translations of the poem and many retellings. There are versions in most European languages and in Japanese, Arabic, Bengali, Malayalam (a language of southern India) and Latin. Some translators have felt that a prose version of *Beowulf* would distort the original less than verse. Others have tried various poetic forms including ballad and blank verse. In 1999 the Nobel Prize-winning Irish poet Seamus Heaney made a highly praised verse translation that captures the vigour and music of the original and is a fine piece of poetry in its own right.

*A scribe at work, as shown in a manuscript of around AD 700*

# HEROES AND MONSTERS

For many years Anglo-Saxon specialists studied *Beowulf* mainly for what it could tell them of the language and history of the period. They didn't think very much of it as epic poetry. Its story wasn't truly heroic, according to their notions. The plot, they said, had not much in it: Beowulf kills a monster, then a second monster, and fifty years later he kills a third. Apart from that he does nothing much. They also felt that the author had made a bad choice of subject – a tale about killing monsters was childish stuff.

They were all the more disappointed because it is clear from the poem that its author knew all manner of tales of Norse kings and heroes, involving clashes of loyalty, betrayal and revenge – truly tragic themes that deserved an epic telling. These partly historical events are mentioned only in passing in the poem (and hardly at all in this book – there isn't room!) as a background to the monster-slaying. As one dissatisfied critic put it: 'The poet puts the irrelevances in the centre and the serious things on the outer edges.'

Then in 1936 a professor at Oxford University named J. R. R. Tolkien gave a lecture which turned *Beowulf* criticism upside down and changed it for ever. He said it was nonsensical to suppose that an author who wrote so movingly about what it means to be human did not know what he was doing when he chose a subject to convey his theme. His monsters and dragons have a universal meaning which a story about some particular clan warfare could not have. They represent the final threat that waits for everyone in this life – death. For pagans like Beowulf there was no hope of escaping this threat in the end.

## DRAGONS

The dragons of the Western world, as we have inherited them from Norse mythology, are totally evil – unlike the fearsome but protective Oriental dragons. This makes them well suited to embodying the doom of all things mortal. Tolkien placed a very high value on them. He claimed that truly, gloriously terrible ones, of central significance to the story they are in, are surprisingly rare creatures. He could only name two such dragons in all of Western literature.

Top place he gave to the treacherous, gold-stealing Fafnir, slain by the most famous of all northern heroes, Sigurd the Volsung (later known as Siegfried). The Icelandic sagas and later German versions of them have guaranteed Fafnir's renown. The runner-up was Beowulf's dragon.

Perhaps the name J. R. R. Tolkien rings a bell and you've already realised that he's famous for much more than giving an influential lecture. He was a respected Anglo-Saxon scholar who took to writing novels (to entertain his children in the first place) and over the years produced *The Hobbit*, *The Lord of the Rings* and *The Silmarillion*. *Beowulf*, he said, was one of his most valued sources for these books. Smaug, his first dragon-creation, in *The Hobbit*, is directly based on Beowulf's dragon. Just like that monster, Smaug is aroused by the theft of a cup; amidst all his treasure he can tell at once that that one thing has gone, and goes on the rampage as a result.

Later Tolkien went on to create other dragons, as part of a whole new mythological universe that was largely inspired by the world of *Beowulf*.

# BEOWULF TODAY

Man-eating monsters, melting swords, underwater battles and a hero of superhuman strength have kept the Beowulf story alive in countless retellings, some very faithful – like Michael Morpurgo's children's version of 2006 – some much less so. Several film makers have been tempted by the story's potential for epic action and special effects, though almost all feel they have to add a love interest.

The 1999 film *The Thirteenth Warrior* is taken from Michael Crichton's 1976 novel *Eaters of the Dead*. This retelling combines the Beowulf story with material from an actual 10th-century account written by an Arab traveller who met a party of Vikings during his journey up the River Volga. (In the real-life account, the Arab writer found the Vikings' general behaviour and standards of hygiene disgusting.) Instead of Grendel, the hero has to face a race of prehistoric cannibals called the Wendol. In the film he defeats them in an epic battle.

Also from 1999 comes *Beowulf* with Christopher Lambert, a fantasy science-fiction version in which Hrothgar has an affair with Grendel's mother, Beowulf falls in love with Hrothgar's daughter, and Grendel's mother is consumed in flames which destroy Hrothgar's castle and everyone in it.

The 2005 film *Beowulf and Grendel*, filmed in Iceland, reinterprets the story in favour of the monsters. Grendel, a well-meaning troll, needs to avenge the death of his father whom Hrothgar and his warriors had killed for stealing a fish. Beowulf has doubts about killing him and finally gives him a burial with a marker over his grave to honour him.

The 2007 *Beowulf*, a computer-animated film directed by Robert Zemeckis, has Angelina Jolie digitally recaptured as Grendel's mother, providing Beowulf (Ray Winstone) with plenty of love interest. He also gets to marry Wealhtheow after Hrothgar's suicide. The film presents Beowulf as a person full of faults rather than a hero. Ray Winstone said in an interview: 'I had the beauty of not reading the book . . . I didn't have any of that baggage to bring with me.'

*A digitally enhanced Ray Winstone as Beowulf in the 2007 film directed by Robert Zemeckis.*

In an indirect fashion the poem gives a lot of background information about its characters which it has not been possible to include in the main part of this book. The writings of early medieval historians give us more clues. Here is some of that information.

### THE DANES

**Scyld Scefing** is probably a legendary figure. According to the 12th-century historian William of Malmesbury, he was the founder of what became known as Hedeby – an actual Danish town of importance in the Viking world.

**Heorot** may also have been a reality. Medieval chroniclers (history writers) say that Lejre, on the island of Zealand in Denmark, was the chief residence of the Scyldings (Danes), Hrothgar's tribe. Lejre is now only a tiny village but three large Viking halls have been excavated there, the earliest dating from the mid-6th century, exactly the period of *Beowulf*. In the poem it is hinted that Heorot is doomed to be destroyed by fire through a family feud – probably the one between Hrothgar and his son-in-law Ingeld, described below.

**Hrothgar**, king of the Danes, is mentioned in Danish histories of the 12th century, and in the 14th-century Icelandic saga of Hrólf Kraki. Both Danish and Icelandic traditions agree with the writer of *Beowulf* that this king was the son of Halfdane and that he lived at the time of the Swedish king Eadgils, whose 6th-century burial mound still exists. So there may really have been such a person as Hrothgar in the 6th century, the period in which the story of *Beowulf* is set.

**Wealhtheow**, Hrothgar's queen, was his second wife, which is why she is much younger than her husband. Women don't get much of a look-in in *Beowulf* except as dutiful queens who are cheerful and capable hostesses. Women were regarded as potential 'peace-weavers': by marrying into rival families they served to create ties of friendship between tribes.

**Freawaru**, Hrothgar's daughter, was used in just this way. When Beowulf visits Hrothgar's court she is already engaged to Ingeld, a member of a rival tribe, the Heathobards. Ingeld's father had been killed by the Danes, and the marriage is designed to cement peace between the tribes. In the poem Beowulf doubts that this arrangement will work, and prophesies that Ingeld's duty to his wife's family will not outweigh his followers' thirst for revenge. The poem's listeners or readers, familiar with these stories, would know that he is right: old wounds will be re-opened. This is another of the hints of doom that shadow the poem. Was this the feud in which Heorot was destroyed? The poet doesn't tell us – he expects his audience to know these things already.

### THE GEATS

The Geats, Beowulf's tribe, were a seafaring people living in the south of Sweden. As the poem suggests, they appear to have been conquered later by their neighbours and to have disappeared from history.

**Hygelac**, king of the Geats, was a historical person who raided Frisia around AD 520. The invasion was recorded by Bishop Gregory of Tours in his *History of the Franks*. Gregory was born not long after the raid, so his information may be accurate.

**Beowulf**, Hygelac's nephew, is praised throughout the poem as mild and just. Nevertheless he is bound by the warrior code to fight to the death in his lord's quarrels. Late in life he is proud to remember how he defended Hygelac in Frisia, slaughtering the enemy's standard-bearer by throttling him with his bare hands.

When Beowulf reaches Hrothgar's court, the king is reminded of Beowulf's father **Ecgtheow** whom he helped in the past. Ecgtheow had killed a member of a neighbouring tribe, the Wulfings, and his own people, wanting to avoid a feud, had banished him. He took to the sea and was sheltered by Hrothgar, who settled the feud by paying the Wulfings the dead man's *wirgild* (compensation for a man's death – in other words, the valuation put on his life). In going to Hrothgar's aid, Beowulf was repaying one good turn with another.

**Wiglaf** is described as Beowulf's kinsman and the last of their clan. Though Beowulf is much older, they are first cousins, Beowulf's mother being Wiglaf's aunt. Scandinavian tribes were composed of many clans or families; Beowulf and Wiglaf belonged to the clan of the Wægmundings – the descendants of a hero of long ago called Wægmund.

## THE SWEDES
The Swedes, one of many tribes living in what is now modern Sweden, were involved in long-running feuds with their southern neighbours the Geats

– just as the Frisians were. Their hostility is often mentioned in the poem, with dark forebodings of the threat they will pose to the Geats when Beowulf is no longer alive to protect them.

The feud began on the death of King Hygelac's father, which encouraged the Swedes to raid. Hygelac and his brother led a counter-invasion in which the Swedish king **Ongentheow** was killed. The Swedes retaliated while Headred was king of the Geats, and killed him. Beowulf was then obliged to pursue the feud to avenge Headred.

Archaeologists in Sweden have found the grave-mounds of Ongentheow, who was buried in AD 510–515, and of his grandson Eadgils, buried in 575. These dates fit in with the events described in the poem.

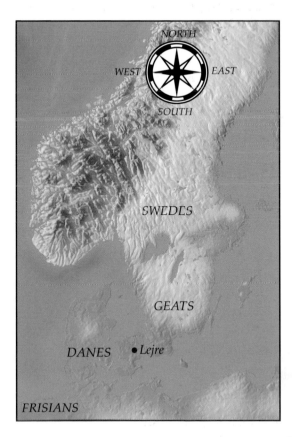

# INDEX

IF YOU ENJOYED THIS BOOK, YOU MIGHT LIKE TO TRY THESE OTHER GRAFFEX TITLES:

*Adventures of Huckleberry Finn* Mark Twain

*Dr Jekyll and Mr Hyde* Robert Louis Stevenson

*Dracula* Bram Stoker

*Frankenstein* Mary Shelley

*Gulliver's Travels* Jonathan Swift

*Hamlet* William Shakespeare

*The Hunchback of Notre Dame* Victor Hugo

*Jane Eyre* Charlotte Brontë

*Journey to the Centre of the Earth* Jules Verne

*Julius Caesar* William Shakespeare

*Kidnapped* Robert Louis Stevenson

*The Last of the Mohicans* James Fenimore Cooper

*Macbeth* William Shakespeare

*The Merchant of Venice* William Shakespeare

*The Man in the Iron Mask* Alexandre Dumas

*A Midsummer Night's Dream* William Shakespeare

*Moby-Dick* Herman Melville

*The Odyssey* Homer

*Oliver Twist* Charles Dickens

*Romeo and Juliet* William Shakespeare

*A Tale of Two Cities* Charles Dickens

*The Three Musketeers* Alexandre Dumas

*Treasure Island* Robert Louis Stevenson

*Twenty Thousand Leagues Under the Sea* Jules Verne

*Wuthering Heights* Emily Brontë